50 Flashcards $7.95

FlashCards

D0508776

FLORIDA
High School
SCIENCE

Preparing Students for
FCAT and Sunshine
State Standards

©2005 Hollandays Publishing Corporation  HOLLANDAYS
Publishing Corporation

A. What is the valence shell of an atom?

B. A valence shell is filled when it has eight _____.

C. The chemical properties of an element are determined by its _____ configuration. Explain.

1

A. The valence shell is the outer shell of an atom.

B. A valence shell is filled when it has eight **electrons**.

C. The chemical properties of an element are determined by its **electron** configuration. The number of electrons in the element's valence shell determines how it will react with other elements.

1. Ionic Bond or Covalent Bond?

    A) Electrons are shared between two atoms.

    B) Electrons are transferred from one atom to another.

2. Elements from opposite sides of the periodic table generally form ionic bonds due to differences in

_____.

1. **A)** Covalent
   B) Ionic

2. Elements from opposite sides of the periodic table generally form ionic bonds due to differences in **electronegativity**.

Which causes a change in phase?

A) Increased heat energy

B) Increased chemical activity

C) Increased kinetic energy

D) Increased space between molecules

C) Increased kinetic energy causes a change in phase. Increased heat energy may result in molecules having greater kinetic energy.

A. List some factors that can increase or decrease the speed of chemical reactions between atoms and molecules.

B. How does decreasing the pressure on a gas affect its reactivity?

C. What is a catalyst?

D. How do catalysts affect the amount of energy needed by chemical reactions?

A. Temperature, concentration, surface area available for reaction, pH, pressure

B. Decreasing pressure on a gas lowers its temperature and increases its volume, so the gas becomes less reactive.

C. A catalyst is a substance that accelerates a chemical reaction.

D. A catalyst reduces the amount of energy needed for the chemical reaction to start.

A. Draw a simple model (Bohr model) of an atom showing the placement of the nucleus, protons, neutrons, and electrons.

B. Which part gives the atomic number of the element?

C. How would you make your atom an ion? An isotope?

A.

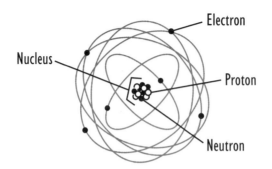

Electron

Nucleus

Proton

Neutron

B. The number of protons (in this case, 6) gives the element its atomic number.

C. An atom becomes an ion (electrically charged) when it loses or gains an electron. An isotope has extra neutrons, increasing the mass of the atom.

A. What is an **element**? Give an example.

B. How are **atoms** and **molecules** related to elements?

A. An **element** is a basic substance made of a single type of atom. Hydrogen, oxygen, carbon, and gold are all elements.

B. Molecules are chemical combinations of two or more **atoms**. Hydrogen and oxygen can combine to make a molecule of water (H_2O).

Radioactive decay causes atoms to give off subatomic particles. What type of radioactive decay produces each of the following?

A. One electron and one antineutrino

B. A particle with two neutrons and two protons

C. Electromagnetic waves

A. Beta decay

B. Alpha decay

C. Gamma decay

Which elements are in the following groups on the periodic table?

A) Metals
B) Non-Metals
C) Noble Gases

1) Helium (He)
2) Potassium (K)
3) Silicon (Si)
4) Silver (Ag)
5) Neon (Ne)
6) Nickel (Ni)
7) Arsenic (As)

A) Metals:
2) Potassium
4) Silver
6) Nickel

B) Non-Metals:
3) Silicon
7) Arsenic

C) Noble Gases:
1) Helium
5) Neon

1. Define a wave.

2. What are particles?

3. Name some types of waves.

4. Which type does not need matter to travel?

9

1. A wave is a traveling disturbance that transfers energy from one place to another.

2. Particles are the smallest pieces of matter in the universe. Electrons, protons, and quarks are all particles.

3. Some types of waves include sound, seismic, water, and light waves.

4. Light waves do not need matter to travel.

A roller coaster car has _____ energy at **A** and
_____ energy at **B**. If there is friction between the
car and the track, some of the mechanical energy is
transformed into _____ energy. With or without
friction, the total energy in the system is _____.

A roller coaster car has **potential energy** at **A** and **kinetic energy** at **B**. If there is friction between the car and the track, some of the mechanical energy is transformed into **thermal** energy. With or without friction, the total energy in the system is **conserved**.

If the average kinetic energy of the molecules in a 5-kilogram bar of steel is tripled, what happens to the temperature of the bar of steel?

11

The temperature triples. The temperature of an object is proportional to the average kinetic energy of that object.

Put these electromagnetic waves in order based on their wavelength (longest to shortest).

- Radio waves
- Gamma rays
- X-rays
- Microwaves
- Visible light
- Ultraviolet light
- Infrared light

longest   Radio waves

Microwaves

Infrared light

Visible light

Ultraviolet light

X-rays

shortest   Gamma rays

1. Explain the first law of thermodynamics (conservation of energy).

2. True or False? A system can do work without a transfer of heat energy. Explain.

13

1. Energy can be converted from one form to another, but the total amount of energy stays the same.

2. **False.** A system cannot do work without a conversion of energy, and some energy is always converted to (and given off as) heat.

1. Define **fission** and **fusion**.

2. Fission or Fusion?

      a) New elements being formed in the intense heat of stars

      b) Neutron hitting uranium-235 to release energy

      c) Power generated in a nuclear submarine's reactor

3. Which of the four basic forces is responsible for fission and fusion?

1. **Fission** is a reaction that produces energy when heavy radioactive nuclei split apart into fragments that together have less mass than the original isotopes. **Fusion** is a process in which two nuclei come together to form a third, larger nucleus, releasing energy.

2. a) fusion
   b) fission
   c) fission

3. the strong force

1. Joe is walking along the road at 3 km/hr. A car traveling in the same direction passes Joe at 40 km/hr.
   What is the car's speed relative to Joe?

2. Alex takes a ferry from the North Carolina coast to Cape Hatteras. As the ferry travels east at 18 km/hr, Alex walks from the front of the boat to the back at 4 km/hr.

   a) What is Alex's speed relative to the ferry?

   b) What is Alex's speed relative to the ground?

1. 37 km/hr

2. a) 4 km/hr
b) 24 km/hr

State Newton's Laws of Motion.

1. Unless acted on by an outside force, a body at rest remains at rest and a body in motion remains in motion. (Inertia)

2. Change of motion is proportional to the force used to produce the change.

3. For every action there is an equal and opposite reaction.

A. What is **acceleration**?

B. Explain the difference between **positive** acceleration and **negative** acceleration.

C. A speedboat accelerates in a straight line from rest to 78 meters/second in 12 seconds. Calculate the average acceleration of the speedboat.

A. Acceleration is any change in velocity. Acceleration equals the change in velocity divided by the change in time.

$$a = \frac{V_2 - V_1}{t_2 - t_1}$$

B. Positive acceleration is an increase in velocity; negative acceleration is a decrease in velocity. Speeding up is a positive acceleration; slowing down is a negative acceleration.

C. 6.5 m/s^2

A. What is Newton's Law of Universal Gravitation?

B. Compare your weight (the force of gravity) on the surface of the Earth to your weight on the surface of the moon.

A. Between any two objects in the universe there is gravity that is proportional to the masses of the objects and inversely proportional to the square of the distance between them. The more massive the two objects are, the greater the force between them will be, and the farther apart they are, the less the force will be.

B. Your weight on the moon would be about 1/6 of your weight on Earth.

A 10 kilogram bowling ball is dropped from a height of 6 meters above the ground. What is its acceleration as it falls toward the ground?

19

Acceleration due to gravity is always equal to 9.8 m/s^2, regardless of the mass of the object or its height when released.

A. An electric current can be created by moving a _____ into or out of a wire loop.

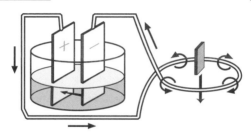

B. A magnetic field will cause moving charged particles to change _____ but not _____.

A. An electric current can be created by moving a **magnet** into or out of a wire loop.

B. A magnetic field will cause moving charged particles to change **direction** but not **speed**.

A. Name the four fundamental forces in the universe.

B. Put these forces in order according to strength (strongest to weakest).

C. Which of these forces can be observed by humans?

D. Which of these forces are nuclear?

21

A. & B.

strongest **1)** Strong force
2) Electromagnetic force
3) Weak force
weakest **4)** Gravitational force

C. Gravitational force and electromagnetic force

D. Strong force and weak force

Newton's third law of motion states, "For every action, there is an equal and opposite reaction." When you ride a bike, several forces balance each other. What are they?

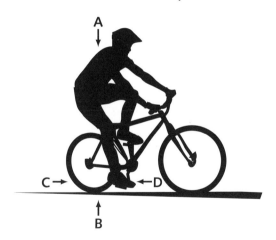

A. Your weight plus the weight of the bike

   Weight = mass (kg) x gravity (9.8 m/s²)

B. Normal force

C. Friction from the bike tires against the ground

D. The force you apply to the pedals

List some causes of weather.

- **Solar energy** (heats air and land)

- **Elevation** (temperature falls with increased elevation)

- **Nearness to large bodies of water** (humidity and temperature are affected)

- **Temperature** (determines how much water vapor air can hold)

- **Air pressure** (produces wind and air mass patterns)

A. Explain the theory of plate tectonics.

B. How does the movement of tectonic plates change the Earth's surface?

24

A. The Earth's crust is made up of thin, rigid plates that float on mantle materials across the surface of the Earth.

B. Tectonic plates can collide. One plate can slide under another, or two plates can sideswipe each other. These collisions can cause earthquakes, volcanoes, and the creation of mountains. Plates can also pull away from each other, causing the spread of the sea floor.

1. What are fossils?

2. In what kind of rock are most fossils found?

1. Fossils are the actual remains or traces of organisms that once lived.

2. Fossils are usually found in layers (strata) of sedimentary rock.

How do these forms of pollution affect organisms and their habitat?

A. Run-off from farm fields into rivers and lakes

B. Acid rain caused when airborne pollution combines with water droplets

C. Sewage dumped into rivers and oceans

A. Fish swimming in polluted rivers and lakes can absorb chemicals like insecticides. Birds, animals, and humans eat these fish and spread toxins through the food chain.

B. Acid rain causes damage to plants. It also changes the pH and chemical composition of lakes and ponds. These changes affect the fish, plants, animals, and insects that live in lakes and ponds.

C. Sewage is a fertilizer that can cause plants such as algae to grow faster than they can be consumed. An overabundance of algae can smother other organisms, including coral reefs.

The Northern Hemisphere of the Earth is tilted toward the Sun in the:

A) Winter
B) Spring
C) Summer
D) Fall

The Earth is the only planet in our solar system that can sustain animal and plant life. Give some reasons why.

C) Summer

Earth is the only planet with liquid water on its surface. Earth's atmosphere contains oxygen, nitrogen, and carbon dioxide, which are necessary for life. Carbon dioxide traps heat in Earth's atmosphere and keeps the surface of the planet warm so that plants, animals, and water do not freeze.

1. It takes about 14 hours to drive from Orlando to Washington, DC (850 miles) at 60 miles per hour (mph). If a spacecraft flew at the same speed from the Earth to the moon (about 250,000 miles), how long would it take to get there?

2. The fastest spacecraft actually travels at 30 kilometers per second, or 67,108 mph. At that speed, how long would it take to get to the moon?

1. About 4,166 hours, or 174 days (traveling 24 hours per day)

2. About 4 hours

1. How are stars created?

2. How do stars produce energy?

3. What are the four stages in the death of a star similar in size to our Sun?

1. A new star forms when a huge cloud (made of hydrogen and other matter) collapses in space. Gravity at the center of the new star creates great heat.

2. The intense heat inside a star causes the hydrogen protons to move so rapidly that they join together (fuse). This process, fusion, is a nuclear reaction that creates energy. The star starts to glow.

3. As the star's fuel is depleted, it expands to become a red giant. The star's outer layers drift away and form a planetary nebula. As the star's core continues to cool and shrink, it becomes a white dwarf. When all of the star's heat is gone, it is called a black dwarf.

Arrange these cosmic objects from largest to smallest.

- Planet
- Galaxy
- Universe
- Star
- Solar System

- Universe
- Galaxy
- Solar system
- Star
- Planet

1. What is an astronomical unit (AU)?

2. What is a light year?

3. What unit of measurement is used to measure distances within the universe?

4. What unit of measurement is used to measure distances within our solar system?

1. One AU is equal to the average distance between the Earth and the Sun (about 150 million km or 93 million miles).

2. One light year is the distance that light can travel in a year.

3. A light year is used to measure distance within the universe.

4. An astronomical unit is used to measure distances within our solar system.

1. What is the name for a protein molecule that triggers and controls a chemical reaction in a cell?

2. How does this protein molecule lower activation energy to speed up a chemical reaction?

1. enzyme

2. Enzymes attach themselves to reactant molecules. The enzyme may bring the reactant molecules together in a particular sequence or it may break down the chemical bonds within the molecules, which speeds up the chemical reaction.

Match each process with its example.

1. Homeostasis

2. Energy transfer

3. Transportation of molecules

4. Disposal of waste

5. Synthesis of new molecules

A. Kidneys filter nitrogen from cells.

B. Amino acids link to form proteins.

C. Light energy is converted to chemical energy in glucose.

D. Water moves through cell membranes.

E. A dog pants after a long run.

1. **E** (Homeostasis refers to balance in an organism. The dog pants to cool off and return to normal temperature, to restore its system to balance.)
2. **C** (This example describes photosynthesis.)
3. **D**
4. **A**
5. **B**

1. How are the processes of **cellular respiration** and **photosynthesis** related?

2. Is **photosynthesis** an energy-acquiring process or an energy-releasing process?

3. Is **cellular respiration** an energy-acquiring process or an energy-releasing process?

1. Cellular respiration gives off carbon dioxide and water, which are the raw materials for photosynthesis. Photosynthesis gives off glucose and oxygen, which are the raw materials for cellular respiration.

2. Photosynthesis is an energy-acquiring process.

3. Cellular respiration is an energy-releasing process.

Name some external stimuli that can affect the growth patterns of plants.

light, gravity, temperature, amount of rainfall, soil pH

Tay-Sachs disease is a genetic disorder that results in a breakdown of the nervous system and death at an early age. The disorder is caused by a recessive gene.

The two members of a certain couple are both normal, but each is a carrier of the recessive Tay-Sachs gene. Use a Punnett square to determine the probability of this couple having a child with Tay-Sachs disease.

A = normal gene a = Tay-Sachs gene

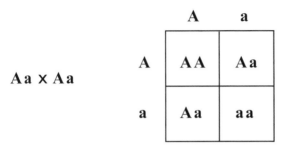

	A	a
A	AA	Aa
a	Aa	aa

Aa × Aa

The probability that this couple could have a child with Tay-Sachs disease (aa) is ¼.

Reproduction: Asexual or Sexual?

1. In _____ reproduction, a single parent gives rise to one or more individuals.

2. In _____ reproduction, two parents give rise to the development of new individuals.

3. _____ reproduction involves the joining of two specialized sex cells.

4. In _____ reproduction, all offspring are genetically identical.

1. asexual
2. sexual
3. sexual
4. asexual

$$\text{DNA} \xrightarrow{\textit{transcription}} \text{RNA} \xrightarrow{\textit{translation}} \text{Protein}$$

1. Explain how *mRNA* is produced through **transcription**.

2. Explain the roles of *mRNA, tRNA,* and *ribosomes* in the **translation** of the genetic code to a protein.

1. A segment of DNA unwinds and separates to expose the bases along each strand. *mRNA* is formed as the enzyme RNA polymerase moves along the coding DNA strand and pairs free RNA nucleotides with their complementary DNA base. The completed *mRNA* separates from the DNA and moves from the nucleus to the cytoplasm.

2. In the cytoplasm, *mRNA* attaches to a ribosome. *tRNA* is a molecule that has an exposed nucleotide sequence (anticodon) on one end and a specific amino acid on the other end. *tRNAs* place specific amino acids along the *mRNA*. As the amino acids are aligned along the *mRNA*, a peptide bond links them together to form a protein.

Arrange the steps of producing recombinant DNA in the correct sequence.

1. Two DNA fragments join together by base-pairing.

2. DNA fragments from a bacterial plasmid and from another source are isolated.

3. DNA ligase pastes the DNA fragments together.

4. DNA from two sources are cut with the same restriction enzyme.

The sequence is **2, 4, 1, 3.**

- DNA fragments from a bacterial plasmid and from another source are isolated.

- DNA from two sources are cut with the same restriction enzyme.

- Two DNA fragments join together by base-pairing.

- DNA ligase pastes the DNA fragments together.

Natural Selection

Suppose a population of small lizards lives on an island of black volcanic rock. The lizards range in color from light gray to dark gray. As birds of prey feed on the lizards, they choose the light gray ones far more often than the dark gray ones. What will most likely happen to the skin color trait in this lizard population over many generations?

In this situation, the dark gray lizards are better adapted for survival. Over time their numbers will most likely increase while the number of lighter gray lizards will decrease. The accumulation of favorable variations in a population illustrates natural selection.

Describe the roles of **producers, consumers, and decomposers** in an ecosystem.

Give an example of each.

41

Producers make their own food. Plants and algae are producers.

Consumers are organisms that eat other organisms. Animals and protozoans are consumers.

Decomposers break down waste and the remains of dead organisms. Bacteria and fungi are decomposers.

Which of these statements about the carbon cycle is incorrect?

a) Plants and animals return carbon to the air during respiration.

b) In photosynthesis, plants take in carbon dioxide from the air.

c) After organisms die, carbon remains trapped in their tissues.

d) The burning of fossil fuels releases carbon dioxide into the air.

C is incorrect.
As decomposers (such as bacteria and fungi) break down the remains of a dead organism, carbon from the tissues of the dead organism is released into the air.

1. What are fossil fuels?

2. Match:

   A) coal

   B) oil or
   natural gas

   1) created from the
   remains of plants

   2) created from the
   remains of organisms

   3) found where oceans and
   rivers were located

   4) found where swamps
   were located

1. Fossil fuels are burnable energy sources that come from the compressed remains of plants, animals, and other organisms.

2. A) 1, 4 – Coal is created from the remains of plants that lived in swamps.

   B) 2, 3 – Oil and natural gas are created from the remains of organisms that lived in the oceans and rivers.

What are some ways in which coastal flooding can affect Florida ecosystems?

44

Coastal flooding can erode beaches, drown plants and animals near the coast, and increase the salt content of freshwater lakes and swamps. This can damage or kill the plants and animals that live there.

Birds' beaks and feet have adapted to allow them to easily get and eat their food. Match each beak/feet combination with the diet that it supports. For each beak/feet combination, name a bird that has these characteristics.

Beaks and Feet

1) Sharp beak and curved talons

2) Flat bill and webbed feet

3) Short, strong beak and small feet

Diet

a) Insects that burrow in the mud

b) Small mammals that scurry along the ground

c) Seeds found on plants or on the ground

Beaks and Feet	Diet
1) Birds of prey (hawks)	= **b**
2) Waterfowl (ducks)	= **a**
3) Songbirds (sparrows)	= **c**

Match the following effects on ecosystems
to their possible causes:

a) acid precipitation   ___1. habitat destruction

b) biomagnification   ___2. nitrogen and sulfur oxides from
power plants and vehicles

c) global warming   ___3. increased levels of atmospheric CO_2

d) loss of biodiversity   ___4. chlorofluorocarbons (CFCs)

e) ozone thinning   ___5. ingestion of pollutants by organisms at
the bottom of a food chain

1. d
2. a
3. c
4. e
5. b

Organize the following steps to scientifically solve a problem:

1. Develop a hypothesis.
2. Ask a question based on observations.
3. Draw conclusions.
4. Test the hypothesis.
5. Plan a test with materials and methods.
6. Do background research.
7. Report findings.
8. Record and analyze data.

2, 6, 1, 5, 4, 8, 3, 7

- Ask a question based on observations.
- Do background research.
- Develop a hypothesis.
- Plan a test with materials and methods.
- Test the hypothesis.
- Record and analyze data.
- Draw conclusions.
- Report findings.

The bicycle was invented in the 1800s. Over time, many people tried to make new and better bicycles. They changed the size of the wheels, the position of the rider, and the way the pedals worked. Later, they changed the design and materials of the bike frame.

How is the development of the bicycle similar to many other inventions?

Many people contributed ideas and improvements to the design of the bicycle. It took a long time to find a design that worked well. Initially, people were limited by the materials and tools they had to work with. As those technologies improved, people could make bikes differently. Now there are many kinds of bicycles for different purposes.

1. How do scientists and inventors affect one another's work?

2. New scientific findings are read and approved by other scientists before they can be published in science journals. What is this process called? Why is it important?

49

1. Inventors can use known scientific principles to make something work better or to create new tools. Scientists can use those inventions to determine new scientific principles and information.

2. The process is called a peer review. Peer reviews allow scientists to identify possible errors in a research study or flaws in the researcher's conclusions before the new findings are published.

Last year, Farmer Jones got a greater yield from Better Bean soybeans than from Super Bean soybeans. This year, Farmer Jones wants to find out if Better Bean plants really are better than Super Bean plants.

Which statement could be a hypothesis for his experiment?

a) Better Bean soybean plants have a longer germination period than Super Bean plants.

b) Farmer Jones should plant with half Better Beans and half Super Beans, then see which kind produces the greater yield.

c) Better Beans produce a greater yield per acre than Super Beans because Better Bean plants have more beans per plant.

The hypothesis (c) suggests a possible reason for the greater yield, which can be tested by an experiment.

Dear Parents,

Here's how to use these flashcards to help your child prepare for the **FCAT :**

- Use the flashcards regularly. Practice 15-30 minutes each night for several weeks before the test.

- Discuss the flashcards. New discoveries in science have led to many changes in the content that is taught in science class. If some of the information is unfamiliar to you, ask your child to explain some of the new content. Offer real-life examples of the terms and ideas that are familiar to you.

- Make a check mark on a flashcard each time your child answers that card correctly. After several sessions look for flashcards with no (or few) checkmarks. Discuss these with your child and seek help from the teacher for these skills.

- Read the advice to the students on the reverse side of this card and urge your child to follow it.

ISBN 0-9753239-8-9

Dear Student,
Here are some
ideas to help you
on the **FCAT:**

- Practice reading graphs, tables, and diagrams. Use examples in your science textbook for practice. Many questions on the test require that you read a graph, table, or diagram, so it is very important to practice.

- Talk to your teacher at least two weeks before the test if you need help with any of the terms or ideas on your flashcards.

- Read the test carefully. Don't just skim. Read the question and all responses before you answer.

- Take your time and check your work.

- Come to the test rested and ready.

Remember to study your Flashcards for 15 - 30 minutes every day for a few weeks before the test.